Para Sandra —

esperando que con
grupo de español tan agradable

ENCHANTED ISLANDS:

Saludos,

TALES FROM THE GALAPAGOS

marzo 2019

ENCHANTED ISLANDS:

TALES FROM THE GALAPAGOS

Ann Merivale

© Ann Merivale, 2015

Published by Ann Merivale

All rights reserved. No part of this book may be reproduced, adapted, stored in a retrieval system or transmitted by any means, electronic, mechanical, photocopying, or otherwise without the prior written permission of the author.

The rights of Ann Merivale to be identified as the author of this work have been asserted in accordance with the Copyright, Designs and Patents Act 1988.

A CIP catalogue record for this book is available from the British Library.

ISBN 978-0-9932970-0-7

Book layout and cover design by Clare Brayshaw

Front cover: Photograph: Large Tortoise looking at the Author

Back cover: Photograph: Lava Field

Prepared and printed by:

York Publishing Services Ltd
64 Hallfield Road
Layerthorpe
York YO31 7ZQ

Tel: 01904 431213

Website: www.yps-publishing.co.uk

For Adam and Hannah, and all those of their generation,
who will in due course, I hope, take over from ours
in efforts to conserve this beautiful planet.

CONTENTS

ABOUT THE AUTHOR

ANN MERIVALE started writing seriously in 1993, following the receipt the previous year of a reading from the distinguished American clairvoyant Aron Abrahamsen (who had worked with Edgar Cayce, widely known as the 'Sleeping Prophet'). To her astonishment, he told her that she had come "partly as a writer – to disseminate information on the spiritual life". Her children were then aged eighteen, sixteen and thirteen, and she was deeply engaged in anti-racist activities and other issues of Justice and Peace.

Previously a Romance linguist, she gradually became increasingly interested in healing, and in 1998 she obtained a Diploma from the London College of Past Life Regression Studies. This was followed in 2001 by a Diploma in Deep Memory Process therapy from the renowned Jungian psychotherapist, Dr. Roger Woolger. She has practised her therapy in both Hull and Ludlow (where she now lives with her husband, David Pearson, who is an Emeritus Professor of Mathematics of the University of Hull, and Surya, their Cavalier King Charles spaniel), but at present her main practice is at the Ripon Natural Health Centre, N. Yorks. The couple now have three grandchildren.

Her first book, KARMIC RELEASE, was published in 2006, and ENCHANTED ISLANDS (by far the shortest) is her seventh. Always a keen traveller, Ann's husband's retirement has enabled her to journey further afield, and nowadays she finds that, whenever she feels a strong urge to visit somewhere in particular, there is invariably a reason for it that is in some way connected to her writing. She also writes a monthly blog for John Hunt Publishing. These are on a wide variety of topics and can all be found online on OMBS Blogs.

ACKNOWLEDGEMENTS

Firstly I owe a big 'thank you' to my friend and loyal reader, Non Davies, for the idea of turning these tales into a little book.

For the factual information about the Galápagos I am indebted to Henry Nicholls, whose book *THE GALAPAGOS – A Natural History* is rightly recommended as *the* one to read on the subject, to the beautifully illustrated BBC Book by Paul D. Stewart, *GALAPAGOS – The Islands that Changed the World*, to Google and Wikipedia, and – last but by no means least – to all the Ecuadorian guides whom we met there.

Like everyone else, I am grateful to David Attenborough for his very many years of service to wildlife and his inspirational television programmes.

I am also grateful to Journey Latin America, who organised our wonderful 'Albatross' trip.

A talk given by Michael Leach to the Ludlow Wildlife Society was also useful.

For his ever willingness to bounce off ideas and make useful suggestions and comments, I am indebted, as always, to Mark Young, my homoeopath, osteopath and good friend.

For advice on the choice of photographs, I am grateful to both my husband David and my daughter Alice, and to the latter I am also grateful for technical assistance.

It was my friend Sarah Edwards who suggested mentioning Indra's Web, and she, who is also a writer, is always a good support too in all my endeavours.

INTRODUCTION

....the perspective of western science is that of a solely material world which is random and meaningless and in which consciousness is merely the accidental outcome of arbitrary evolutionary processes.

Such a limited, disempowering and frankly wrong outlook has brought us and Gaia to the edge of destruction.

Dr. Jude Currivan ('HOPE – Healing Our People & Earth')

When I was at school, the subject I hated most after Mathematics was Geography. I found it utterly boring and, since I was so bad at it, was not even permitted to take it to O Level (now GCSE). Not having Maths O Level either considerably limited my choice of university, but fortunately Bristol, in 1959, was willing to accept Biology as sufficient scientific qualification for doing an Arts degree. I studied French and Spanish, and the second half of our first year had to be spent at the Sorbonne. The idea of a term and a half in Paris was exciting, but when I heard that, of the four courses we had to choose, the only compulsory one was French Geography, my heart sank! Yet we all found those particular lectures enthralling and, though I've long forgotten most of what I learnt during the three years of my degree course, a few of the things that that Sorbonne Geography lecturer told us are still indelibly engraved on my mind. Geography should always be an enthralling subject, and I reckon that at my school it was just (like Maths!) very poorly and unimaginatively taught. (I have no doubt that massive improvements have been made in schools since my day.)

Maybe it was because of my lack of education in the geography of any part of the world other than France that the first time I even remember hearing of the Galápagos Islands was when I was in my forties. I had heard of Charles Darwin of course, but where he had travelled to hadn't really seeped into my consciousness. However, a university colleague of my husband's named Nadine (now long deceased) once went to Ecuador for a conference and she took advantage of the trip to visit the Galápagos Islands. We met her at a party not long after her return, and she talked enthusiastically about them. At the time I was very busy rearing three young children and working on Justice and Peace issues in my spare moments, and so I never pursued the matter. The only thing that really stuck in my mind from what Nadine said had to do with the giant tortoises she had seen there. Somehow I vaguely visualised those tortoise-populated islands being just a few miles from Ecuador – visible from the coast in fact – but at that point a seed was sown in my mind about "going there one day".

It was not until after the summer of 2004, following my adoption by Shropshire, that I learnt that Darwin had been born in Shrewsbury (the county's capital and only thirty miles from Ludlow, where we live now) and been educated at Shrewsbury School prior to going to Edinburgh University (and later of course to Cambridge). Shrewsbury's public library is now housed in the original school building, and the Darwin statue positioned outside it can easily be seen by anyone walking up the main road from the railway station. He apparently always described himself as a "born naturalist", and even to this day the fields and the River Severn surrounding Shrewsbury are still open areas filled with flora and fauna. Darwin also acknowledged that his childhood experience of growing up in Shropshire, which has rocks from more different periods of geology than anywhere else in the world, had helped to develop his inquisitive mind. And another point of particular interest to me is that, until she sadly died when the young Charles was only eight, Darwin's liberal mind was probably encouraged by his mother, with whom he attended the Unitarian church in Shrewsbury (founded in 1662). Unlike average Christians, Unitarians are renowned for their acceptance of very varying beliefs.[1] (I have also found out the reason why I myself feel so very much at home in Shropshire, but that will be discussed in my *next* book!)

By the time that the seed sown by our friend Nadine had really taken root and grown, our three children had become independent, thus improving our financial circumstances, and one or two television programmes had again brought these 'Enchanted Islands' to my attention and also taught me a little bit more about them. By that time too I had achieved my ambition of 'doing Peru' and completing the Inca Trail, as well as travelling quite a lot in India. At one point China had reached the top of my travel wish list, but then, for some unexplained reason, China suddenly got temporarily pushed down the list in favour of Ecuador and the Galápagos. We had been so happy with our Journey Latin America tailor-made trip to Peru in 2005 that I decided to book with them again, but this time choosing their Albatross Tour rather than selecting all our destinations ourselves. After the small hiccough of suddenly needing to have a breast cancer operation, and the larger hiccough of our travel insurance company taking forever to pay up, this wonderful trip was finally realised at Easter 2013. There were just seven of us in the group, with a marvellous, bilingual, very

knowledgeable, tour guide for the mainland and, after spending three days on our own in Quito trying to adjust to the time difference as well as catch up on sleep and acquaint ourselves a little bit with the capital, David and I joined the others and spent a fascinating week travelling slowly south to Guayaquil, where we reluctantly said "goodbye" to our guide Adrian. The background in this photo of him is typical of the mainland scenery through which we were fortunate to have been driven.

Adrian Gallop

One of the things for which the large city of Guayaquil is most celebrated is the giant iguanas that inhabit the *plaza* (square) outside

Guayaquil iguana

the cathedral. Adrian took us to see them at dusk (just in time for a photograph!) after walking us up well over four hundred steps through the beautifully renovated *favelas* for the marvellous view, and prior to a very tasty farewell dinner. These creatures were a good foretaste of what lay in store for our following week's tour, but they also rather rapidly became overshadowed by it.

Guayaquil favelas

We had a disagreeably early start for the airport the next morning, so the most copious breakfast I have ever seen in my life was sadly wasted on us, but all that delicious-looking roast turkey, salmon, cakes and fruit was eventually forgotten in the excitement of landing on Baltra at the end of a 600-mile flight. (I had by now already learnt that the Enchanted Islands were certainly NOT visible from the coast of Ecuador!) We were destined to spend our precious week sailing around the islands in a comfortable, though not luxurious, boat named Coral I, with twice daily disembarkations, and our group of seven expanded to nearer thirty. A motley crowd of people of very varied ages and nationalities bonded rapidly with the aid of first-class cuisine washed down by whatever anyone wanted from the bar, a competent and friendly crew, and extremely well informed local guides, who talked us through each impending landing, giving us as much information as we could possibly digest and then some. Rarely have I been so excited, and I soon learnt too that April was a preferable time of year weather-wise than would have been October. (So my little brush with cancer had been well timed!)

Each disembarkation involved quite a feat of athleticism, first from Coral I into the *pangas* (dinghies) and then from the *pangas* to either a wet or dry landing on whichever island was on the agenda for that morning or afternoon. (On one occasion the dry landing was followed instantly by a wet bit!) David and I managed okay, but after getting home I put it about that I did recommend doing the trip *before* the age of seventy if possible. Wet and dry landings obviously required different footwear and, though recommendations for this were always given

Panga

Dry-wet landing

Walk over lava field

in advance, occasionally another change was necessary if, for instance, a wet landing was followed by a walk over a lava field.

It was magical seeing the birds, iguanas, sea lions and fur seals (all so well described by David Attenborough in particular) at such close range, but it was still the sight of Nadine's giant tortoises that was my greatest ambition. The first attempt at this had to wait until Day Three, and even then a sighting was by no means assured. So the realisation of such a long-held dream (perhaps inevitably!) brought forth the writer's pen and then – to the writer's own intense surprise – Carlo the tortoise suddenly spoke through it. He was followed not long after by the Frigate Bird, who took upon himself a challenge issued not long before our departure by Mark, my close friend and homoeopath. At our most recent meeting I had remarked that I "could never write a novel", partly because I was "no good at thinking up metaphors". The challenge he then gave me with regard to making an attempt at fiction will be taken up in my ninth book (though that still won't be a novel!), but in the meantime it seems that the Frigate Bird had taken seriously Mark's exhortation to "enjoy playing with language". (He had commented "After all, you *are* a linguist!") The Albatross came through immediately following our return home. After all, since the Galápagos *belong* to the birds and animals, should it not be they who are given the opportunity to speak for them?

After typing their words up and circulating them by email to various friends as well as to the other members of our Journey Latin America group, I was left wondering what to do with them. One of the staff members of Journey Latin America, to whom I also sent the pieces, replied saying that he hoped I would publish the material "since it was educational as well as interesting. " Then I went off to France for the 2013 *Mouliners'* meeting (see *LIFE WITHOUT ELGAR – A Tale of a Journeying Soul*[1]) and there my good friend Non said to me "Why don't you publish the pieces as a tiny book, complete with a few of your photographs?" So I pondered the matter and then decided to add a further couple of tales, just to make the book a tiny bit less tiny, and in due course, after *THICKER THAN BLOOD?*[2] had been completed following a seven plus-year haul, the Sea Lion and Spider obligingly put their oars in. The ensuing pages are consequently our joint effort. I hope you will firstly enjoy our heroes' words and secondly feel inspired – if not to visit these magical islands for yourselves – at least to make a contribution to their preservation as well as to that of the rest of our precious planet. For my part I shall be donating any proceeds from the sale of this little volume to the Galápagos Conservation Trust. So, if you do enjoy it, you might consider also buying copies as gifts for your friends.

Finally for a little word about the photographs. I have never (at least in my present lifetime) been at all artistic and, much though I would love to have time to do a digital photography course, I have never had great aspirations in that field. We upgraded our Canon camera especially for this trip, but it is still not nearly as powerful as any camera that a professional photographer would use. In any case, when we were preparing for it, the idea of the tour resulting in a book could not have been further from my mind. Since, however – probably more than any other trip that I have ever done – our experiences in the Galápagos were largely so very, very visual, and also since this book is so tiny, it would seem to me to be a pity if it did not give the reader at least a small idea of some of what we saw. It's not as though there were no other means of seeing really good photographs of Galápagos wildlife. The BBC book mentioned in my Acknowledgements is superbly illustrated, and there are of course nowadays so many excellent wildlife programmes shown on the television. No doubt TV documentaries about the Galápagos will go on coming round again and again. My amateur photos are therefore intended to be no more than a little taster!

So please take what you can from my humble offerings, and may blessings be upon you and upon all the precious wildlife of this amazing planet.

Notes

1.   See my book, *LIFE WITHOUT ELGAR – A Tale of a Journeying Soul*, 6th Books, 2014. Helen Weaver, Elgar's first love and fiancée, was a Unitarian.

2.   *THICKER THAN BLOOD? – A Fresh Look at Adoption, Fostering and Step Families*, 6th Books, 2015.

A TORTOISE'S TALE

In the long history of humankind (and animalkind) those who learnt to collaborate and improvise most effectively have prevailed.

Charles Darwin

My name is Carlos – after Charles Darwin, who made these Galápagos islands so famous. They haven't always been named that. In the now fairly distant past, when people tended to be more spiritually minded than most are nowadays, and believed much more in magic and so on, the early sailors who came to our part of the Pacific thought that the islands weren't there all the time. This was because they couldn't see them when they were shrouded in mist, and so they called them the *Enchanted Islands*, or *Islas Encantadas* in Spanish. It was only later that Spanish colonists to Latin America decided to name the islands after the many tortoises they saw there. Many people say that, because some of us have developed 'saddlebacks' on account of having to grow longer necks in order to reach food growing higher up, the islands were named after the Spanish for saddle: 'galápago'. (They think that 'saddle' best describes the shape of the shells of these particular tortoises.) However, in actual fact it was the other way round! You see galápago is both the old Spanish word and the zoological term for what most Spaniards now know simply as a 'tortuga', or tortoise in English.

I myself am not a 'galápago' (N.B. with a small 'g') tortoise; they're smaller than I am and live on different islands from mine. That of course is what so fascinated that Darwin bloke and inspired his seminal work. If his famous theory of 'natural selection' is correct (and I personally have no reason to doubt it), we have all developed different characteristics and appearances according to the nature of the terrain of the island upon which our direct ancestors landed and the vegetation growing there. Your friend Darwin was quite quick to notice the fact that the species here vary so much from island to island. I am what is known as a 'dome-backed tortoise', and people call me a 'giant'. Well, I suppose I do have many smaller cousins in other parts of the world, and I think it must be mainly because of my size that nowadays so many people come and gawp at me. I've been here on Santa Cruz for a very long time (about 175 years in my present body), and generations of my ancestors were here for centuries and centuries before I was born. Rumour has it that my first forefathers just floated across to these volcanic islands from Chile, sitting on various clumps of vegetation, leaving behind the dramatic background of the Andes, settling happily here among this much more gentle scenery, and then breeding. Our lava-rich soil has over millennia become a very fertile ground for the many different varieties of seeds blown over the Pacific from the mainland, and the consequent rich diet provided for us, combined with lack of stress and *lots* of time on our hands, have permitted us to grow much larger than our Chilean ancestors ever did.

To start with life out here in the middle of the Pacific Ocean, astride the Equator, was completely paradisic. (The Galápagos Islands are of course unique in the world in having no indigenous human inhabitants.) We and a handful of other creatures had this whole wonderful world to ourselves. Though rain falls at certain times of the year, it is always either pleasantly warm or hot here; food, as I have already made clear, is abundant, and there never used to be anything at all to worry about. Gradually over the centuries more and more species came to join us, but none of them ever gave *us* any trouble.

Trouble only began when the species that considers itself to be at the top of the evolutionary ladder suddenly 'discovered' our lands. They came across from the same sorts of places that my and the other species' ancestors had drifted or flown from, but they came in things called boats and, when they reached our precious islands, they stood up and walked on two feet. The biggest problem was that they were thirsty and hungry and, for some strange reason, they weren't content with the delicious cacti and other vegetation that had kept us happy and well-nourished for so many centuries. Since these isles are short of fresh water, we had developed a good way of storing a plentiful supply of it under our shells. Alas, those creatures who called themselves 'human beings' (the word 'humane', which looks so close, didn't seem to come into their vocabulary!) soon discovered our secret supplies and drank them all up. And that of course involved removing our precious, protective shells, the consequence of which was that many of us were left to die.

Worse still, these human beings then decided that our flesh was good to eat. On land they satisfied their hunger by decimating us and then, not content with that, when setting off to return to their own lands, they took vast numbers of us into their boats with them when they set sail. We tortoises are frugal and can survive for a long time on only a little food and drink, so the sailors, as I believe they call themselves (because of the fact that those early boats were powered by wind and sails), just killed us off one by one when their supplies were running low and they wanted more meat to eat. What would they have thought if *we* had eaten *them?* The thought of this massacre really makes my blood boil! Doesn't it yours?

These facts are stored somehow in my genetic memory. Or maybe I actually was myself once one of those poor tortoises who got consumed to abate the sailors' hunger? No doubt I have had numerous lives before this present, rather long one, and why should I ever want to reincarnate as anything other than a tortoise? Those human beings think themselves superior simply because they have more developed brains, have learnt to navigate by the stars and to solve complex mathematical equations. Nowadays they don't even need to study the stars because they have things called computers and 'GPSs' that do all the work for them, but what good has it ever done them? They may have got to the moon, but it *isn't* made of cream cheese; they still have to exploit this Earth in order to feed their ever-growing population and (no longer being content with wind and sails) fuel their new-fangled boats and other vehicles.

So, while their population was growing out of all proportion, ours was dwindling drastically. We saw no need to eat them, yet they thought they could not survive without eating us! Gradually some of the inhabitants of mainland Ecuador (the country which in due course decided that they actually *owned* the Galápagos Islands – as though any land could be owned by anyone but the Creator!) decided to come and live here. During my 175 years or so I have personally seen the human population of our islands more than quadruple – to something over 25,000. Of course you can't really blame anyone for wanting to make this idyllic place their home, just as my forefathers did after having landed on one or other of the islands, but my ancestors and all those who have succeeded them have *never* destroyed anything here. We've witnessed what you can call 'natural destruction', when the Nazca Plates have collided yet again and caused these lands' many volcanoes to erupt and new islands to be formed, but we have only ever consumed things that grow quite quickly again of their own accord.

Human destruction, on the other hand, has been so great that it even caused at least one line of my tortoise cousins to become extinct. When these people came to their senses and suddenly realised that Lonesome George on Pinta Island was the last of his kind, they tried desperately to rectify the situation, but alas they were too late. All their efforts to find dear George a suitable mate were to no avail; he was impervious to all the feminine wiles and charms that were proffered, and he died in 2012 still a lonely bachelor with no progeny. Let's hope that no similar fate befalls any of the rest of us! I myself at least have several descendants, I'm proud to say. Not that I take any interest in any of them now. Why should I? They have their lives to live and I have mine. We don't believe in co-dependency like those impoverished human beings!

And talking of human beings, it's not only the inhabitants of mainland Ecuador who have been flooding over here in recent years. Every single day now – in fact about thirty times a week – huge metal birds descend from the sky on to, for instance, Baltra Island (home to nothing but an army base and loads and loads of cacti), and there they vomit, not from their mouths but from their bellies, hordes and hordes of tourists of all different sizes, shapes and colours. These rainbow people in turn get on to buses and clamber into *pangas* and then swarm over our islands during the day like flies on cow dung, spending their nights in boats and/or hotels. (Not all the islands yet have hotels, thank goodness, but we have them here on Santa Cruz, which is home to the Charles Darwin Research Station as well as being very close to Baltra.) In my lifetime I have seen these tourists increase so much in number that I've long since given up trying to keep count of them. Not that their gawping presence really bothers me anyway; I simply ignore them all and just carry on living peaceably in the way that I and my predecessors have always done.

Having got all that off my chest, however, I must admit that there has been *some* improvement, in that the tourist industry is now fairly strictly regulated. These people, who apparently pay a great deal of money to come here, are obliged to stick with a guide who is a 'professional naturalist' (that means someone who has studied us in depth and think – usually correctly, I believe – that they know a great deal about us. And when I say "us" I mean the birds, sea lions and so on as well as us tortoises). And they are not allowed to come too close to any of us. Nor are they allowed to drop litter or take even so much as a grain of sand away with them. That's partly why *none* of us need to bother ourselves in the slightest about them. (I've heard it said that in these tourists' own lands the human beings have over the centuries caused the birds and the beasts to fear them so much that now they fly or run away as soon as anyone begins to approach them. If that's really true, then it's no wonder they get so excited when they come here!)

Yesterday a woman called Ann came to my area (known as Ballena Bay on account of the whales that sometimes pass by). She's a writer and she really loves travelling, though it seems she wouldn't describe herself as a 'travel writer' like so many people I've seen over the years. She and her husband joined a tour named the 'Albatross Trip', organised by an excellent agency called Journey Latin America. (They'd already been to Peru with JLA some years before and been delighted with it.) They were in a group of only seven at first, and a man called Adrian, whom they all liked very much and whose Spanish is just as good as his English (something which Ann, with her rusty degree in Spanish, greatly envies), guided them through various interesting sites on the mainland for a week, ending up in Guayaquil, Ecuador's largest city. There he led them up a hill that has 444 steps and then, not content with that, up a lighthouse. It was well worth it for the view and the interesting sight of the brightly painted and pleasantly restored *favelas*, but Ann (being 73, which is not young, it seems, by human standards!!!) found that as a result her legs were suffering when she reached our Galápagos the next day. However, she wasn't going to let that put her off taking part in anything: she's someone who likes challenges and is always determined to do and see *everything*. So of course, when the Coral I boat brought her together with a rather larger group of people to Ballena Bay, she was dead set on seeing one of us so-called 'giants' in the wild. Her 'Albatross Trip' group and the other passengers of Coral I had already been taken to the Santa Cruz Tortoise Breeding Centre, where they had been able to photograph a few of my baby relatives, but these human beings always seem to think that nothing quite equals seeing creatures 'in the wild'.

Baby tortoises at the Charles Darwin Research Station, Puerto Ayora

At this point I think I should explain that the people who now co-habit the Galápagos with us – or a good group of them at any rate – are endeavouring to compensate for the damage done by their predecessors. One of the things they are doing in their attempts to make amends is to replace the multitudinous tortoises who got murdered in the past. So they breed them at a place called after my namesake and then, when the youngsters are old enough to be independent, they let them loose to fend for themselves on one of our islands. In this way they are hoping ultimately to rectify our seriously reduced numbers.

By now you human readers may well be wondering how I, with my "small tortoise brain" (disproportionate to my size compared with yours!), know all this. Well, this woman Ann that I've just been talking about, has been studying spiritual matters for many years and has taken an interest in shamanism. She consequently appreciates that things may not always be as they seem from external appearances – that 'inner life' is in fact even more important that 'outer life'. My, Carlos', body may only have been endowed with quite a small physical brain, but I am nevertheless linked in to something very powerful that we could call the 'group tortoise consciousness'. Or 'group soul' if you like. You know how your great human psychologist, Carl Gustav Jung, talked of "universal consciousness"? I think he understood better than many about the Spirit – I like to think of it as the Breath of the Creator – that pervades *everything* in the universe.

So Ann, our writer friend, was when she stepped, awestruck, on to our precious soil, doing all she could to tune into that. First she uttered a prayer in her head to her God (whom she knows as Sathya Sai Baba, but she is also aware that She/He has countless other names); then she called out to me, Carlos – or rather to a part of our 'tortoise group spirit' – appealing to me to appear on the path that her group was following, so that she could put a little tick on her list of achievements. A tick against the phrase "saw a tortoise in the wild", which was one of the items on her mental list.

I heard her inward cry (we who live here, uncontaminated by the world's so-called 'progress', always hear everything on the etheric level), but I decided nevertheless to teach her a lesson. For, after all, in just one of the many thousands of lives that we live on this planet, there is no need to do *everything*, see everything, experience everything. Indeed that would be totally impossible, however much time and energy one had. The world is too vast and far, far too complex to be understood and appreciated in a single sojourn; we have eternity to get to the bottom of it. So it is much better to live in the moment, accepting whatever comes or does not come as part of what we need for that particular day, and putting all our efforts into experiencing what we are experiencing in the most profound way possible. There can be nowhere on Earth where it is easier to do that than here in the Galápagos. These islands may be on a "conveyor belt" (as one of the Coral I naturalist guides describes it), from volcanic birth in the hot spot to lingering death a lot further east, yet here we offer our visitors the opportunity of experiencing a profound and wonderful sense of time having stood still. Isabela, where Coral I is heading for next, is a 'youngster' in the great scheme of things, while Española, which Ann and her companions have already visited, is at present in her death throes (long drawn out though they may be), but that need not make us sad. It is just the way of the world, and what is death but Transformation?

So my message to Ann, and to all those who come or hope to come to this unique and miraculous world, is not to worry the slightest about what you see or don't see. Just enjoy the delightful, comical sight of the blue-footed boobies even if you don't have the opportunity of seeing a red-footed one. Let the pure air, the warmth and all the spectacles around you penetrate to the depths of your being and, before returning to your overly-busy lives in your own countries, lock the memories of these experiences safely into a secure place deep inside you – one to which you will be able to return at any time for the rest of your life. And finally: remember that – to your eyes at least – I, Carlos, do not look very different from my giant friends whom you saw already at the Breeding Centre.

Two days later

Now I have a happy postscript to my tale! I am glad to say that I have just heard on the tortoise grass (our equivalent to your grapevine) that our friend Ann took my lesson well and was amply rewarded for it. I mentioned that the boat her group was in was heading next for Isabela (which is the largest of our islands by a long chalk, and the second most westerly after Fernandina and therefore the second youngest). Well, after disembarking at Tagus Cove on huge, seahorse-shaped Isabela, and walking up to Darwin's Lake, and then later in the day making a brief call at Punta Espinosa on neighbouring, even younger, Fernandina, (Thorny Point to you, but I'm not really quite sure how it got its name. Was Espinosa another politician?), they returned to Isabela the next day. There they went in the morning to Elizabeth Bay, where they stayed in the *pangas* and drifted around the mangroves gazing at the tiny lava islands as well as all the amazing wildlife. Much though she loved observing the blue-footed boobies, herons, pelicans, sea lions, turtles, mullet, and the impressive red-throated frigates flying overhead, what Ann appreciated most about that excursion was the feeling of utter tranquillity in that tiny portion of the Pacific; that particular stretch of our magical lands felt to her like a true Paradise on Earth.

Coastal journey

So that was one great reward for accepting not having seen *me* just two days earlier, but the same day, when they landed in the afternoon in Bahia Urvina (named certainly after an Ecuadorian president), the party was provided with a much appreciated contrast to their morning excursion. They had been told by their guides that it

Teenager in a hurry!

was the time of year when tortoises, who mate in the uplands during the rainy season, begin coming down from Volcano Alcedo to the lowlands in order to lay their eggs. The members of the group were warned, however, not to have too high hopes of seeing any. Well, you can imagine the party's absolute delight when, before very long, they had completely lost count of how many of us they had seen! Twice their narrow route got

Author and her husband with a large tortoise

barred: once by a mere teenager, who firmly made his clear and determined way between them all, next by a 250-kg elder, who made it quite clear that he had absolutely no intention of moving off the path that he rightly regarded as his. Yet this elder did nevertheless deign to let them all be photographed in turn either beside or behind him. At another point there were five of us to be seen huddled together underneath a tree, while another tree was sheltering a large tortoise carcass.

Cameras of course clicked endlessly (what will they all do with all those images, I wonder?), but Ann at first felt a little bit sad that her camera was not able to get the tortoises' heads into her pictures very clearly. Once again, however, she was in luck because, before too very long, one of my

9

relatives decided to have a really good stare at them all, pushing his neck right out and gazing fixedly and motionlessly ahead of him. Ann returned his gaze and – to her immense surprise – was momentarily overwhelmed by a feeling of true communication with a kindred spirit. (It was this that made her, after deciding to produce a book, want to have that particular photograph on the front cover.) Despite her absolute horror at the thought of tortoises having been slaughtered for human consumption, she had never previously thought of us as either "beautiful" (in the way that many of our birds are beautiful) or remotely "on her wavelength". Yet, thinking afterwards about this encounter, she remembered her friend Mark recounting a similar experience of communication upon seeing a crocodile on a river bank in Malawi, and then she reminded herself of the great poet Keats' lines *"Beauty is truth, truth beauty," – that is all ye know on earth, and all ye need to know*[1]. In other words, she understood (what some of our Galápagos naturalists also understand when they communicate with, as well as observing, us) that, different though we all may be in appearance, and different though our roles and purposes may be, we are not only all equal in the eyes of the Great Spirit, but also all PART of that Spirit. Many of us (especially the human ones!) have forgotten whence we originally came, but NOW is the time for re-remembering. Darwin's theories of 'natural selection' and the 'survival of the fittest', which led him to understand and then expound a now well accepted concept of evolution, are one side of the story. The other, which has been well understood and expounded for thousands and thousands of years in countries such as India, concerns evolution of the *soul* through mineral, vegetable and animal to human (and eventually 'super-human', once the soul is finally ready to return to Source). Now is the time for these two equally important aspects of Life to become integrated and acknowledged, for only when they have been will our beautiful planet be able to return to the Primeval Magnificence that we, the Giant Tortoises and our fellow creatures of Galápagos, exemplify.

Even bigger!

P.S. Perhaps, however, the biggest tortoise of all is this one, which they saw on Santa Cruz on the very last day, just before being taken back to Baltra for the return flights.

Note

1   From John Keats' ode *On a Grecian Urn.*

A FRIGATE-BIRD'S TALE

Both great and magnificent frigatebirds have huge wings relative to their body size. This might make for an awkward lolling gait and an ungainly, flapping take-off, but once airborne it allows them to stay aloft for long periods, cover great distances and reach speeds of around one hundred miles per hour.

Henry Nicholls (from 'THE GALAPAGOS –
A Natural History')

....The oppressive heat hung heavy on my tormented brow
Then we saw.

Unsteady at first; Pirouetting
countless circles; unravelling
the same number in hypnotic display.
Aerobatic to the last
It skims the ocean limit. Landing;
I see a crest of gold, straggling
Behind in awkward flight.
Two berry-red eyes flecked
With yellow grains of incandescent light. The helmet
Of limbate black and blue.
Its back two feet limp: High and rising
Flexing its serpentine back,
Higher, it spirals skyward,
A speck against a cloud.
Fast, it moves decisively, pausing
It turns its head.

Big, the magnificent frigate bird, plunges
Headfirst. It lunges;
A dizzy streak of black
It punches the water; calm, the water
Envelopes the bird. Quiet – A minute
Passed. We waited. As though we had witnessed a dream.
Nothing stirred. Only the ocean; Suddenly
Like a phoenix, born from the ashes,
The Magnificent frigate bird emerged, gaping,
Its mouth, the steely vice, clamping
the catch. Spray, streaming
profusely off the firm swallowtail,
Cascaded to ringlets on the water, calm
The ocean smooth; it calms the senses,
The magnificent bird is gone. A dream.

From a poem written by Jonathan Kershaw when he was sixteen years old and having an exciting holiday in Florida. Seeing Magnificent Frigatebirds for the first time, flying over the Florida Keys, made a great impression on him.

I am a frigate-bird. Call me 'Fragata' if you like; it more or less rhymes with Renate – one of the lovely ladies who was on the Journey Latin America Easter 'Albatross Trip'. Fragata. It sounds much nicer in Spanish, don't you think? Just as *mariposa* is a *much* prettier word than 'butterfly'! Not that anyone is quite sure of the origin of the English word; one theory is that it is simply 'flutter by' accidentally metathesised. Can one make a verb from the noun 'metathesis'? I'm not sure, but I *am* sure that people do all sorts of funny things with the English language nowadays! When was 'impact' first made into a verb? *Very* recently. I hate it myself and see it as people having just got lazy with their language. What's so difficult about saying "has an impact on"? Still, I suppose one does just have to accept certain developments and changes in language that take place over the years! Although I dislike this new-fangled confusion between nouns and verbs, I abhor even more what my writer friend Ann calls the "nominative bug", which she complains has recently reached pandemic proportions in the numbers of people in the English-speaking world who have caught it. It may be difficult to avoid catching a 'flu bug if you're already a bit under the weather, but she reckons that a bug which involves using one's brain ought to be quite different! Why, Ann wonders, do people always have to be sheep? Saying something that's so obviously incorrect just because other people do? This new 'bug' or linguistic error is *completely* illogical because no-one would ever dream of saying "He gave it to I". Yet nowadays even many highly educated people are regularly saying or writing things such as "He gave it to David and I." instead of "David and me". Crazy! And it must be very confusing for people of other nationalities who are taught English grammar and then find English-speaking people breaking the rules themselves.

Still, all that is bye-the-bye, I suppose. Now let's get back to the topic of pretty words and insects. *Mariposas*, yes. My favourite one of those on these Galápagos Islands is the bright orange 'Queen'. There are lots of them to be seen on our largest island, Isabela, but they aren't exclusive to it, and they thrive during the rainy season (December to May). Since we have only one species of bee here (the carpenter), all the butterflies – sorry, *mariposas* was our preferred word, wasn't it? – have a particularly important role as pollinators. I don't think the group from Coral I who were cruising here during Easter week noticed vast numbers of them, but then they were all concentrating so fixedly on the larger species – the creatures such as sea lions, iguanas, tortoises, herons, hawks and so on, that they never have a chance to get really close to in their own countries. *Papillon* is a nice word too, don't you think? Nicer than 'butterfly' anyway!

Well then, if we're moving into French now, what could possibly be more beautiful than the word *libellule*? So onomatopoeic! It's almost the same in Spanish – *libélula* – and in Italian – libelulla – (both having the stress on the second syllable), yet somehow the French with its more equally measured syllables seems to have the edge for attractiveness. Or for me it does anyway. A lovely word for a lovely creature! Just let it roll around your tongue and then see in your mind's eye the glint of those amazingly coloured dragonfly wings as our sun shines brightly upon them and allows them to glow in a way that cannot be seen so often in greyer countries such as England. Not that we have vast numbers of *libellules* here. That's because of the shortage of fresh water (they don't really like sea water as we frigates do), but they can be seen on San Cristóbal, Santa Cruz, and Santiago as well as on our giant island, Isabela.

Going back to the butterfly now, have you heard of the 'butterfly effect'? Was it Rupert Sheldrake who said that a butterfly flapping its wings on one side of the world would affect things on the other side? He is probably rather an exceptional man among modern scientists, because how many of them really understand about the interconnectedness of *everything* – as (among others) Native Americans always have? (By the way, why is it that, even after all these years since Columbus' big journey across the Atlantic and the subsequent realisation that he had not after all reached the Indian subcontinent, people still insist on calling these people 'Indians'? Or, worse still 'Red Indians'! At least in Canada they are now more respectful of their indigenous population, calling them 'First Nations'.)

The retired Head of the Social Anthropology Department of Cambridge University, Dr. Stephen Hugh-Jones, has spent a very large part of his life living among and researching native Amazonians on the Brazil-Colombia border and, when he was first married, he and his wife did an amazingly adventurous journey into their territory by canoe. He came and gave a fascinating talk about some of his experiences to the Ludlow U3A (which, by the way, in case you don't know, means University of the Third Age) and Ann, my scribe, who was by then long returned from Ecuador, had the good fortune of attending this meeting. The people he talked about live amicably and peaceably together in long houses, exchanging goods with their neighbours rather than depending on money, and Dr. Hugh-Jones and his wife Christine stayed with them for long enough to become accepted, join in with all their daily tasks, and learn their language well. One thing that Ann, as a linguist, found particularly interesting in his talk was the fact that these people always marry outside their own group. There is nothing unusual in this, but what is unusual is that, as each group speaks a different language, this also means marrying someone who speaks a different language from one's own. (Of course all the languages of the area are fairly closely related, so it's not like, say, an English-speaking person marrying someone from China or Japan.) I find it interesting too as an indication of the Amazonians' sense of equality – a thing that, alas, so many people have lost. Their shamans also – like shamanic practitioners the world over, and unlike your average Western doctor – understand that the physical body is not a machine working completely independently from everything else. Real healing can only occur when it's appreciated that the body that can be examined by normal human eyes is no more than a small part of the full picture.[1]

Sadly, when Stephen and his wife Christine returned to the Amazon a few years later with their two children, the one-time rubber gatherers had by then turned their hands to producing cocaine from the Indians' coca leaves. Christine, however, is a strong and determined woman and she succeeded in making contact with the people involved, finding out what they were up to, and documenting the impact of their activities on the Indians' way of life. Of course a whole book could be written on the depressing subject of drug abuse, but I'd prefer to leave that to experts. I would, however, like to lament the North Americans' obsessiveness about coca leaves, which means that no tourist is allowed to take even a single one of them away from the South American continent. This is silly since literally tons of the stuff are needed for making even a tiny quantity of cocaine, and the leaves are not only good for altitude sickness, but they contain more calcium than milk does and they're not mucus forming as dairy products are. I'm not saying that it isn't important to stamp out the use of dangerous drugs such as cocaine, but firstly obsession increases publicity, which could have the effect of actually tempting people to try it, and secondly we always need to remember that making mistakes is part of learning. For sure, the learning often seems dreadfully slow: people who become addicted to drugs during one lifetime may well not get over it as soon as they die, but there is always help available[2] and everyone will learn eventually how best to lead a human life on Earth.

So now what about *me*? Were you thinking when you saw the title of this little piece that I was going to tell you something about myself, just as my tortoise friend, Carlos, did the other day? Well okay then, I will if you like. My full title in English is Magnificent Frigate-bird, and I am endemic to these islands (which means that you won't find another bird exactly like me anywhere else in the world). I am slightly larger than the Great Frigate-bird, and I like to stay closer to the shore than he does. The correct term for that, by the way, is that the Great Frigate-bird is more pelagic than we are; and we are found mainly on the inner islands, while our smaller relatives are more likely to be seen on the outer ones. We are, I think, (or anyway we males are) just as beautiful as the *libellule* I was talking about earlier, but in a totally different way. Our size, and our huge forked tails, obviously make us more impressive than they are, and certainly much more noticeable, and one of the things that Ann and her companions were amazed by was our swooping skills. We have to swoop well in order to catch food such as flying fish from the surface of the water. You see we can't land on water because we lack the oil-secreting gland which keeps sea birds' feathers dry. In that we differ radically from the boobies, and one of the ploys we have developed is forcing boobies to regurgitate their catch for us.

Do you think that's unfair? Would you call it stealing? Well, I think it's perfectly fair because boobies can just plunge straight downwards like upside down rockets and bring up as much fish as they want from underneath the surface of the sea. It's absolutely no problem for them to fish for us as well as for themselves. I know Ann and the others in the group loved watching the boobies' dives (too fast for the cameras unless one has a video!), but I think we are perhaps the ones that they most envied. After all, however young and agile they still are, human beings are always somewhat limited by their two heavy legs. That's why many of them love doing crazy things like hang gliding or bungee jumping – for the momentary sense of freedom that it gives. (Even Ann, at 73, still really loves whizzing down hills on her bicycle.) But we have that freedom *all* the time. The boobies catching fish may be good fun to watch, but we certainly have the edge for beauty in the way in which we circle way overhead so gracefully. (I mean "way overhead" from a human point of view.)

Just compare us with those poor flightless cormorants with their almost useless wings. Their wings weren't always like that of course – it's part of that 'evolution' thing that your great hero Darwin theorised about after coming here – and it's only here, mainly on the east

Group of Cormorants

coast of Fernandina and the northern and western coasts of Isabela, that you can see cormorants with such silly little stumpy wings. It seems that, since they spend so much time on land, where they haven't been troubled

Nesting cormorant with eggs

by predators, and are of course good swimmers, they ceased to be dependent upon flying and so (over very many years I suppose) their wings just shrank to these mere stumps. Ann was fascinated to see one of these birds incubating its three eggs, but, quite apart from hating the thought of not being able to fly, I feel particularly sorry for the male cormorant. He does a huge amount of work, nest building, bringing back food for the family, and also, being larger than his mate, he's better at keeping the predatory hawks away, but then once the chicks are a couple of months old, she just clears off and finds another mate! Typically she'll breed three times in a year, but then I suppose she has to do that because more often than not only one of the three chicks from each brood survives. Their courtship behaviour isn't nearly as impressive as ours either. I'll talk about that in just a moment. The cormorants start off their mating in the sea, just swimming around each other bending their necks, and then they move onto land and go to their seaweed nests, which the male promptly augments with gifts such as bits of flotsam or even bottle caps. Why bother regaling your mate with presents if she's only going to jilt you as soon as she can? Ah well, it takes all sorts!

So what are some of the other birds that are of greatest interest here? Maybe Darwin's finches are the most famous, but really their only real claim to fame is the fact that it was his observation of the differences between the finches of different islands that in large part spurred his research into what he called 'The Origin of Species'. You see it was the varying foods available on each of the islands that, for instance, caused their beaks to develop in different ways and shapes. Darwin collected many specimens from different islands, and was later a bit cross with himself for having been rather lax with labelling them all, but he still had enough information to give him the gist of the theory he gradually developed. The finches aren't particularly striking in themselves; it's simply the fact that they vary in appearance from one island to another that has aroused so much interest. Photographing small birds that don't tend to stay put for very long is difficult, but Ann was pleased with this photo, which the lovely guide Sabina told her was a fly catcher.

More impressive for the Coral I group was the Galápagos Hawk. Having been brought up in Europe or America, where bird behaviour is so different from ours, they could hardly believe how the hawk that they saw in a tree on a beach didn't move a millimetre when they went near to it. That caused real excitement among them! As did the heron on another beach, which stood completely motionless while awaiting the best moment to go and pinch an egg from the numerous turtle nests. (The group had been warned to be very careful where they walked, and were again fascinated when

Yellow-breasted flycatcher

Galápagos Hawk

Heron

Turtle's egg

the guide showed them an egg shell because it looks exactly like a ping pong ball.)

Anyway, the most impressive thing about *us* – us male frigate-birds, that is – is our gorgeous red throats. They come into play mainly during the mating season, when we can inflate them to an incredible degree in order to attract the females. They form such a stark contrast to the rest of our black plumage, and the females with their very inferior white breasts cannot help admiring us and are consequently easily seduced. Not that I'm not choosy of course! I wouldn't want to seduce just any old female; I always study them all first and decide which female looks the most suitable as a mate. Our choosiness, though, is a bit more subtle than the boobies'. Boobies are of course a type of gannet, but what distinguishes Galápagos ones from gannets in other countries is their brightly coloured feet. Their blue or red colouring comes from the algae that they eat, and whether it is blue or red depends upon the type of algae growing in the area in which

Blue-footed boobies

they live. The better their diet, the brighter the colour of their feet, and that is how the females make their choice of mate. The way in which the male boobies show off their feet during mating rituals is considered by human beings to be hilariously funny, and so that is why they acquired their curious name.

Ann is disgracefully ignorant about birds in general, even though she loves their song and the feeling of freedom that they convey, but she had seen us on television before she came here and was very excited the first time that I came close enough overhead for her to be able to see my red throat and consequently be sure that I was a frigate. That first time she tried desperately hard to photograph me, but her camera is a new one and she has yet to get the full hang of it, so she kept just missing the right moment and got very frustrated.

So a few days later I took pity on her and got together with a large group of my friends while the passengers of Coral I were on the top deck. It was a really beautiful day with bright sun and a clear azure sky, which is not always the case during the rainy season, and it was consequently a perfect opportunity for showing off our plumage and our flying and swooping skills to the gullible people who were enjoying the view from the top deck of their boat before going off in the *pangas* for their next excursion. They all got incredibly excited at there being so many of us, and of course everyone had their camera at the ready when we came really close. Ann now felt more optimistic at getting a satisfactory photograph than she had before, but she was still having a bit of difficulty in focusing

in the right direction. So she was very grateful when a young Indian girl sitting next to her offered to have a go with her camera. This girl was more successful in her aim and you should be able to see from the attached pictures that our bright red pouches show up quite well in the air even without being inflated as they are during display. David too, when he took over the camera from his wife a bit later, was pleased with his

Frigate-bird

success. They only just managed to catch one of our females in their camera, and also they would both have loved to have a chance to see our mating ritual, but they accepted the fact that, in just one week, it is impossible to observe absolutely all of our Galápagos delights and treasures. They did their best, however, and I am delighted that they got so much out of their trip!

Female (white breasted) frigate

Notes

1   See my October 2014 OMBS Blog on the Pandemic of Cancer http://www.o-books.com/blogs/obooks/cancer-a-pandemic-by-ann-merivale/

2   See *DELAYED DEPARTURE – A Beginner's Guide to Soul Rescue*, Ann Merivale, 6th Books, 2013.

AN ALBATROSS' TALE

In the beginning, each spirit gave birth two souls; two souls destined to sail across the worlds, over the lands, one clothed by the moon, the other by the sun. That is why each moon seeks its sun, and why each sun weeps for a moon, the ideal image of which it keeps locked in the depths of its heart…

Anne and Daniel Meurois-Givaudan, *Chemins de ce Temps-là*, (translated by the author)

My name is Alba. It's the Spanish for 'dawn'. I believe you also have a girls' name Dawn in English, don't you? I really love the dawn! What can be better than waking up to the rising sun after a good night's sleep, listening to the sounds of some of our fellow feathered creatures, and getting ready for a peaceful day of fishing and observing all that's going on in this glorious ocean? And how aptly named it is – because 'Pacific' of course *means* peaceful! Tross, my soul mate, my true love, my life partner, feels just the same way as I do about the dawn. We've heard that many of you human beings – especially those living in northern climes – often fail to wake up in time for it. What you miss! But Tross says it must be hard for you when it's bitterly cold and grey even when the sun *has* come up. We're more fortunate here in that way. Also, we are particularly fortunate during that part of the year in which we are able to be together. You see, Tross and I, we are two aspects of one being; together we make a whole: an albatross.

We are not like, for instance, the frigate-birds or the boobies, who don't believe in monogamy (though I suppose you could perhaps call them 'serial monogamists'!). Each year, when it gets to the mating season, the male frigates puff up their red chests as far as they can, and the male boobies wave their blue or red feet about to show off their colour, and

23

in this way they endeavour to convince any attractive female who comes near that they are the best candidate for fathering the new generation. How superficial such attraction is! Their relationships rarely, if ever, last more than a single season. With us albatrosses, however, the bonds are very much deeper; we don't look just for external signs of good health and virility. To us not only is strength of character much more important than anything like colour, but we *know* deep inside that we will recognise 'him' or 'her' once we have got to know them. Your human history is full of stories of 'twin souls' or 'soul mates'! Dido and Aeneas, Héloïse and Abélard, Tristan and Isolde, Romeo and Juliet, Robert and Clara Schumann, Robert and Elizabeth Barrett Browning, Richard Burton and Elizabeth Taylor, to mention just a few. Mythical or real, their tales are so often fraught with tragedy, yet even in the midst of tragedy these unhappy lovers are more often than not looking forward to an afterlife in which they will be reunited.

Ann, who is serving as my scribe at the moment, wrote a book on this subject[1]. She was interested in describing and analysing the different sorts of soul-mate relationships, as well as in looking for the lessons to be learnt in even the saddest of stories. Also, as a therapist, she has a great interest in what is known as karma, and often she was able to write about her subjects' previous lives together or even speculate about their joint future. We, however, are not interested in either past or future; we like to live *completely* in the present. After all, what greater 'present' have we than the present? I know that's not original, but I like it, and it is a lesson that could be well learnt by many people! Some of course – I could certainly mention many Buddhists as excellent examples – have already done so, but for those who still have a great deal to learn, I hope that we albatrosses can also serve as a good model.

We are also very different from the promiscuous turtles who swim in our seas. Those poor females think that they need to mate with umpteen males in order to be able to lay countless numbers of eggs each year, believing (apparently rightly) that this is the only way of ensuring the survival of their species. Ann and her husband, whose group had been warned not to walk near the turtles' nests, did indeed watch a heron standing guard over one of them with the obvious intention of stealing an egg or two. Ann and the rest of their group did see some mating turtles when they were drifting around in one of the *pangas*, but getting a good photograph of them was too difficult. She was, however, pleased with this one of a pelican swimming.

Pelican

To the turtles' several hundred, we lay just a single egg, and even that not every year! And I also have to admit that, if the turtles' nests in the sand on the beach seem shallow and inadequate for protection, we have never made a habit of building nests *at all* up here on the cliff. I appreciate that other birds may think us unwise in this, but at least Tross and I and the others of our species do *care* each time about our egg. We don't just clear straight off to sea again the moment we've laid it, as the turtles do. We take it in turns with the incubating, and in the early stages each of us does about three weeks at a time. When our chick first hatches it is the most adorable little ball of brown fluff, and then we feed it by turning the food we catch out at sea into oil in our stomachs before bringing it back to him or her. It takes us over a year to raise a chick. Once our baby no longer needs full time care, we put it into a nursery with all our friends' babies and then Tross and I take it in turns to bring back its food. Well, you members of the human species put your little ones into nurseries too, don't you, while you go off to work? They quickly get used to it, and it's good for them to have company until they're old enough to fend for themselves.

April to December is by far the best time of the year for Tross and me, because, as I said, it is only now that we can be together most of the time. You see, we waved albatrosses of the Galápagos, just like other albatross species, are renowned for our long distance flying (so much so that I understand that certain albatrosses are now being used as models by people who are trying to pioneer new types of aircraft!), and when we're having to travel over vast areas of ocean during the wet season, keeping together is just too difficult. Trossy and I do miss one another when we are apart, but we have no choice when it comes to searching for the best squid and plankton. Besides, just like our tortoise friend Carlos who has already told you his tale, and *unlike* many human beings, we don't believe in co-dependency. We agree a hundred per cent with what 'The Prophet' has to say about marriage:-

"Sing and dance together and be joyous,
but let each of you be alone,

Even as the strings of a lute are alone
though they quiver with the same music."

(That's not of course the most famous quote from Kahlil Gibran's beautiful poem on marriage, but you probably already know by heart the one about the "pillars standing apart"!)

The reason we are so very good at flying very long distances is that we know how to make the best use of the wind with our enormous (seven to eight foot-span) wings. In our case the wind is provided by the cold Humboldt Current, and we can glide on it effortlessly. Five thousand miles is nothing to an albatross! Trossy once even went all the way to Japan, but it made him sad to see the devastating effects of the nuclear disaster they had there – the one that wrought such dreadful havoc at Fukushima. And he's still feeling sad about it now that it's gone out of your news. At first he said "Well, they didn't learn from Chernobyl, but surely they'll now learn from Fukushima!", but alas he soon became less optimistic. He tells me that there are plans afoot for building more nuclear power stations in Britain. Why can't you all just put a lot more effort into harnessing natural resources? I know you can't use wind for travel in the way that we do, and I know that even George Monbiot and James Lovelock are now saying that, at least for the time being, it won't be possible to manage without some nuclear power, but can you not appreciate that wind power is *much* safer? As for the sun, its energy is limitless. Even though you don't get as much of it in your northern climes as we do here, photovoltaic panels on your roofs only need light to make electricity, and if putting them onto every new building became compulsory, your energy needs could be much more readily, *and* much more safely, met.

I know too that you can be dreadfully extravagant with your electricity – especially at times like the run-up to Christmas. Ann and her family used to go regularly to Spain for winter holidays and there they were impressed by the fact that the Christmas lights and other decorations only went up on about December 20th. A huge contrast with England, where the shops try and force people to start thinking about Christmas the moment the summer holidays are over. Take Oxford Street, which is a huge shopping centre in London and people tend to go there from all over England to look for Christmas presents. Ann and David went there in early November 2014 (I'm moving forward a bit now, but never mind – I can still communicate telepathically with my scribe!), not to shop but for a concert at the Wigmore Hall. They were bowled over by the dazzling beauty of the white lights – some going up and down tubes hanging in trees, others (hundreds of them, in different sizes) hanging from the sky just like moons. Yet, they thought to themselves, "How much power must all this be using?" And at the moment they're talking about electricity cuts possibly happening in Britain through the winter!

Trossy, with the wide knowledge he has gained from all his travels, also points out that if only you human beings made better use of wind, sun and waves, you would not need to plunder the Earth for oil. Ecuador is at present getting rich (at least rich by Latin American standards) from oil discovered underneath their beautiful rain forest – they are now even doing deals over it with the Chinese without thought for the potentially disastrous effects on their indigenous people – but who is worrying about what will happen when they've used it all up? It's so silly when, after all, they get enough sun here on the Equator! Ann has just been reading an excellent book by Thom Hartmann entitled 'The Last Hours of Ancient Sunlight'. It not only points out the catastrophic results of all the unthinking plunder that has been carried out in recent years, but also makes very good suggestions as to possible solutions to all the world's present problems. A friend had passed it on to her thinking it to be a book that *everyone* should read and, since Ann agreed with that, she left it in the little library on Coral I's main deck. Let's hope that lots of people read it, and not only on the boat.

Yes, Ann and her husband were surprised when, before flying over (in an aeroplane of course!) to our islands, they were travelling through the mainland and saw so many large, posh-looking houses either newly built or in the process of being built. One of their guides explained to them that it was not only the oil that was bringing wealth to many Ecuadorians, but also that there had in recent years been a mass migration of Ecuadorians to the United States. He said that these people were earning good sums of money up there and sending a lot of it back to their families to build houses with. They have to build them gradually, bit by bit as the money arrives, but the result is quite impressive as you drive down through the Andes and past all those amazing volcanoes.

However, I was saying to Tross just the other day that a better way of making money was surely the Panama hat trade that is practised in Cuenca. After all, the toquilla palm that they use for weaving those hats is replaceable in a very short time – quite unlike what Hartmann calls 'ancient sunlight', which takes millennia to be converted into coal or oil. Hey, that would be a good question for anyone having to compose a quiz: "Where do Panama hats come from?"

"Wrong! They come from Ecuador and were only given that name when people in Panama took to wearing them."

Panama hats

Yes, Cuenca is in a completely different sort of way as good a holiday destination as our islands. It's such a beautiful little city anyway, the countryside around it is really spectacular, and there are so many interesting things to see in that area. Ann had thought that the Panama hat factory might be a bit boring, but far from it! She found watching the fabrication process fascinating and thought the display of hats – of so very many different shapes and colours – to be of great interest even to a 'non-hat' person like herself. Päivi, who was also in the little group with the Journey Latin America Albatross trip, bought herself an unusually-shaped white one, edged with black ribbon, and she looked absolutely stunning in it. And in this picture you can see how popular Panama hats are in Cuenca.

Getting back to us now: here in the Galápagos we waved albatrosses are found only on Española, the oldest island, and that is because it is the only island whose cliffs offer the long take-off and landing strip that

She must really love Panama hats!

we require. We do know that, having over millennia drifted the furthest east of all the islands, Epañola's days are numbered, but we ourselves are unlikely to live beyond forty, and so it won't be during our lifetime that she will gradually sink into oblivion. Our children and even grandchildren won't need to worry about the island's disappearance either, and anyway they will soon learn that only the soul lasts for ever. So there's no point in getting attached to *anything* material. In any case some of our species have already emigrated to Isla de la Plata, much closer to the coast of the Ecuadorian mainland. No doubt they will continue to breed there, and maybe some of them will eventually find other suitable homes. At least nowadays there is an increasing awareness about 'endangered species', and there are good people around (such as the Galápagos naturalist guides) who are sincerely trying to do something constructive about it.

I already told you that Tross and I (like all other pairs in our species) were true soul mates or twin souls. Well, we didn't grow up together, and we didn't find one another instantly; we had to put some effort into our search for one another. As adolescents we albatrosses dance with many partners in succession, just as human beings do, but, unlike you, who either have passionate affairs that bring you terrible heartaches or indulge in sexual experimentation without true feeling coming into it, our dancing forms an important part of our search for our life partners.

Albatrosses

You see – well, I'm sure you have observed – our appearance doesn't differ as much as yours does from each other. We're all roughly the same size and have roughly the same colouring and distinguishing features, and so this makes it more difficult for us to find the partner for whom we are destined. However, just like those human beings who are fortunate enough to be with a soul mate, we always find him or her after a few years of practice. (We feel sorry for people who are not so lucky over relationships, but at the same time we appreciate that you choose different lessons for each of your human lifetimes. Learning to stand alone, which we do for a large part of the year anyway, is always an important lesson.)

I'm sure it must be difficult for you to understand quite why we undertake synchronised performances of actions such as **preening**, pointing, calling, bill clacking, staring, and combinations of different behaviour such as the 'sky-call', but take my word for it: that is how we get to know one another. It's hard to explain, but this is how we come to appreciate another bird's *soul* rather than just his body (beautiful though that invariably is). Then, once these elaborate and painstaking rituals have enabled us to form the pairs intended for our present life, we still have to devise a means of ensuring that we will always be able to recognise each other again in subsequent years. This we do by perfecting an individual language that is completely unique to each couple. Establishing this is of course essential for coming together again once our yearly long distance travels are over. The males come back to Española first, where they wait patiently for us females to rejoin them; and, since we all look so similar, you can well imagine that it is more difficult for us to find one another than it would be for you human beings. It is invariably an intense moment when I make my landing. My mind becomes full of emotions and I find myself asking inside my head "Is Tross really here already? Is he getting frustrated because some of the other females have arrived here before me? Will we have to try out our special language in vain on several other albatrosses before we become reunited?" But these emotions, though natural, are silly really because of course it never (or rarely) takes that long for the reunion to take place.

And how can I describe the overwhelming joy we feel when we are reunited? We always have so much to tell each other about our travels and what we saw, about our thoughts and feelings, our hopes for hatching our next chick, and so on and so on. These wonderful moments are so very precious – much more precious than the gold or diamonds you value so much when you exchange rings as symbols of your love – that they are well worth the agony of separation and the anxiety that precedes each reunion. So my message to you is to savour every moment of joy that you experience on Earth, making the most of it while it lasts at the same time as appreciating that it will not last forever. The great Indian avatar, Sathya Sai Baba[2], pointed out regularly while He was incarnate that "joy is an interval in between two pains" and vice versa. Those who have the good fortune of sharing a lifetime with their twin soul believe, as we do each year when we have found one another again, that they truly know ecstasy, yet this ecstasy is but a pale shadow of what we all have in store when we finally achieve reunion with the Divine. Those who have the 'misfortune' of having met their twin but suffered at his or her hands (either through falling out for some ridiculous reason or simply through silence on the 'other half's' part) can instead work towards experiencing union with the Divine while still on Earth. This is what the Masters all achieved, so it is clearly not beyond human capability. I wish you all perseverance and good fortune as well as rewarding travels!

Notes

1   See *SOULS UNITED – The Power of Divine Connection*, Ann Merivale, Llewellyn Worldwide, USA, 2009.

2   The word 'avatar' means 'divine descent', and Sathya Sai Baba, who was born in Puttaparthi, Andra Pradesh, on 26 January 1926 as a reincarnation of Sai Baba of Shirdi, left His mortal coil on 24 April 2011 but still 'presides' over an enormous ashram in Puttaparthi. His devotees are now awaiting His return as Prema Sai, in the State of Karnataka.

A SEA LION'S TALE

Happiness surveys consistently show that we're happiest when we're serving something beyond and bigger than ourselves.

Dr. Jude Currivan (in 'HOPE – Healing our people and Earth')

Round about Easter time 2013, when I was still a small pup, a group of tourists landed from a fairly small boat named Coral I onto my island (Española, which, as I believe you've already been told, is the oldest). Ann, one of those amongst them, was struck by the whiteness of our sand, and it reminded her of the Whitsunday Islands in Australia, which she and her husband had visited a couple of years previously. Pristine environments like those islands and ours here are such a precious rarity on this beautiful Earth that people like her feel very strongly indeed about the importance of preserving them. Where the Galápagos Islands differ from the Australian ones, however, is in the sheer quantity of wild life that the tourists notice when they disembark onto one of them. And what those people from different countries came to observe on that occasion – and indeed on all the many occasions that tourists land here – is the vast numbers of us living together so peaceably without any thought of doing harm to anyone. They are exhorted by their experienced guides never to get any closer than three metres to any one of us, but Ann found anyway that we were too numerous for it to be possible to come closer. My name, by the way, in case you are interested – I mean the name of my species in human language – is leon marino, but, since I am female, you can call me Leonita if you like. That means "little lion" in Spanish, and I was, as I said, a very young pup at the time that I'm talking about. My mother had gone off to sea to fish that morning; we sea lions need to eat just as you do, and while I was not yet weaned she of course needed even more fish to eat than usual. Unfortunately (as alas happens fairly regularly) I happened

Sea lions' Beach

to get hungry again long before she returned, and so I was searching up and down the beach looking for her, desperately hoping for some more milk. Since we look so alike, a young pup has to learn to recognise his or her own mother's sound straight away, more or less from birth, and our good sense of smell can also help us to track our mother down. But that particular day I was so desperately hungry that I was asking each female in turn whether they could feed me. Those that I approached, however, were all saying "No" to me, sometimes even pushing me away, as is their wont. This upset the Coral I group very much, and our friend Ann even asked their guide, Victor Hugo (sic! But I doubt very much that he is a descendant of the great French writer), about it. His reply seemed horribly harsh to her – "Its mother might come back tomorrow or she might not. ¡La vida es dura!" Well, Ann already knew only too well that life was hard, but that remark was no consolation at that moment either to her or to any of the rest of the group. I think that's really good: compassion is one of the most important things to have. Would that there were more of it in the Middle East at the moment! Human beings often think of it as a characteristic unique to them, but it certainly isn't. Elephants, for instance, have been shown to feel incredible compassion for members of their families who are suffering or dying, and intense grief when one of them does actually die; and cats' healing powers, or dogs' loyalty to their masters and mistresses, can be quite staggering.

The cosmologist, healer and author, Dr. Jude Currivan, comments in her book *HOPE – Healing Our People & Earth* that wider empathy and compassion seem to have early roots. She says that archaeologists from the University of York recounted in 2009 "examples of deep compassion dating back at least half a million years. The material evidence included the remains of a child with a congenital brain abnormality who wasn't abandoned but cared for… And a later Neanderthal who was blind in one eye and had deformed feet and a withered arm was looked after by the community for as long as 20 years." As Jude says, "Such love is the heart of what makes us human.", yet is it not a fact that many people at the moment are not even *trying* to behave as human beings should? Of course everyone at present living on Earth has had previous lives of which they would now be ashamed if they remembered them. Ann, my scribe, thanks to all the work she's been doing in recent years, *does* now recall some of hers; it helps her (*when* she remembers!) to be less judgmental of others. It is through multiple experiences and actions that one learns all one needs to learn, though it is sometimes difficult not to feel sad about the apparent slow progress in the learning. Even some 'New Agers' are at present finding it increasingly hard to believe that the promised 'Golden, Aquarian Age' is really "just around the corner"! We have to appreciate, however, that eternity is a very long time indeed, that the *Kali Yuga*[1] may yet take a while to be completely spent, that it is up to each and every aware person to do their little bit towards healing this precious Earth, and that the ability to do one's "little bit" will not cease with one's next physical death. So, what better title could one have for a book than HOPE?!

At this moment in 2014, there is huge concern over the crisis of the Ebola virus in West Africa, which has already killed so many people, and which is spreading fear of infection in America and Europe as well. One has to have tremendous admiration for those doctors and nurses who risk their own lives in order to go out to Africa to give a helping hand. Rather than feeling totally depressed and worried about it, however, we should appreciate the opportunities that are thus being given to people to exercise caring. Sometimes the carers are paying off a debt from a previous life in which they had been uncaring, and sometimes noble souls volunteer before incarnating to take on a disability or sickness that will give someone else an opportunity to be in the role of carer. The importance of such caring is what Jesus and other Masters and prophets have always taught.

Do you ever reflect upon the strange fact that, although so many of the world's wars are fought on grounds of religious differences, all the great spiritual teachers brought *exactly* the same message? Jesus said "Love thy neighbour as thyself", Sathya Sai Baba said "Love all, serve all. Help ever, hurt never.", the Buddha said "If you truly loved yourself, you could never hurt another".... And did Mohamed say "You should kill all those who do not subscribe to the Muslim faith"? Or that women should be treated as inferior to men? Did Jesus say that it would be wrong to use birth control even if the Earth became seriously over-populated? Or that sexual acts performed with love were a mortal sin? I'm sure that most people yearn for the sort of peace that we sea lions and other species experience most of the time here in these precious islands, and so I hope that those who come here will be able to learn from us and take some of this precious peace home with them.

My personal tale continues happily, however, since my dear mother did indeed return in due course and was able to give me a really good feed once we had been reunited. You can imagine my relief! If I hadn't had a feed soon I might not still be alive to tell you my tale. Many are not so lucky; you see we are carnivores and, since fish is by far the most accessible form of meat for us, we naturally go out to sea to catch it. There, however, we have three main predators: sharks, killer whales and human beings. So long as there's enough to catch close to the shore, we're fine, but when we have to go further out, that's where the danger lies. Compassionate human beings, such as the group I've just been talking about, would be shocked at the idea of killing a sea lion, but alas, as I've just been saying, not all are the same and for some people money (which, believe it or not, can be obtained in exchange for our blubber!) is all important. We love various different sorts of fish – herring, mackerel, salmon… whatever is available really – and when what's most accessible is crabs or clams, we have strong back teeth with which to crack them open.

Another problem is that we – particularly the males (called bulls), who grow to be really enormous compared with us females, easily weighing up to 1500 pounds – have extremely large appetites, and so if the fish supply

Sea lions above beach

grows scarce, sometimes these males feed on sea lion pups. This must seem distressing to you – as indeed it is to their mums (the cows) – but it is part of nature's way of controlling the population. One just has to accept it because, after all, as you saw from the previous photo, everyone who comes here to Española has to admit that there are an awful lot of us on our beautiful beach. Ann's favourite photo, however, is this one.

You very likely know that one of the ways in which bull sea lions *do* resemble some of those men in the Middle East is their habit of keeping harems. For that reason they're never ready to start reproducing before the age of at least eight and it's often nearer ten. You see they have to grow really big and strong first in order to be able to fight off the other males who are also wanting to catch the most attractive females.

I'll very soon be of an age for courtship – how exciting! That's because we girls can be ready to mate by the time we're about three years old – a lot earlier than the males. I hope I'll make a good mother. Then perhaps you who are reading this little book might feel inclined to come over here and admire my offspring. Most of us live to be at least twenty, so you could try asking around for Leonita. The only trouble is, though, that you might have a bit of difficulty understanding our language, even though we communicate so very well to each other. You humans tend to be fascinated by our huge array of sounds. We all use honking and trumpeting noises that are completely intelligible amongst ourselves and, when we feel threatened in any way, we roar really loudly. Then the males bark when they're looking for more mates to join their harems. (For, as well as having a powerful sense of smell, we have excellent hearing both on land and in water.) This must all seem very different to you from your various languages, and I suppose some of it could sound a bit frightening. That's why it works of course! However, I hasten to add that, unlike the sea lion that Ann and David's group encountered when they were looking for kiwis late at night on a beach in New Zealand, we would never pose a threat to groups like yours. If one of us does come a bit close, you only need to clap your hands for us to get the message and turn tail.

Did you know that sea lions were about the most social animals in the whole world? We are extremely gregarious and always live in large groups, really loving one another's company, as you will see from this next photo. We probably couldn't survive on our own, but we do form numerous sub groups, each with its own hierarchy. One's level in the hierarchy depends upon age and so on, so we're not restricted to any one level for life. And, although a harem can contain up to thirty females, there's never any jealousy or competition between them, and the 'wives' will always look after each other after the males have gone. In fact our society could be quite a good role model for your human one, don't you think? Evolution through all the different species may increase intelligence and the ability to do certain things, but does it always increase that important thing I was just talking about – compassion?

Affectionate Sea Lions

There could possibly sometimes be a bit of confusion between sea lions and seals, and the main differences are that seals are smaller, crawl on their bellies rather than walking on flippers as we do, are happiest in cold water, have no external ears, are not very sociable, and are rather quieter than we are. The Galápagos Islands are, however, home to a type of pinniped (that means 'fin footed' if your Latin is rusty) known as 'fur seals', who are in fact members of the same family as ours. Like the penguins and other cold water species, it is only thanks to the cold Humboldt Current that they ever came here. Even though we're all Otariidae (another Latin name of course – too bad they no longer teach it much in most of your English schools! People call it a "dead language", but it's an important part of your heritage.), we don't tend to meet because they prefer lying on rocks, which cool them down after they've emerged from the sea. The human group that I've been talking about saw some from a boat at the same time as they saw the small penguins who are related to Chilean Humboldt penguins and that also live on the lava coasts of Fernandina, Isabela and Bartolomé.

Now, talking of lava, on the afternoon of the day on which the Coral I group spent such a long time with us, and after Ann had had a wonderful swim while her non-swimming husband had returned to the boat early, they all came back to Española for a three-kilometre 'lava walk'. They had been warned to put on very good footwear, and they were able to borrow sticks from the boat's stores, but that apparently didn't stop the walk from being extremely tough. We simply couldn't do it at all despite our efficient flippers. (I always feel quite offended by human beings laughing at the way we walk. They should admire the valiant efforts we make with our short flippers, as well as realising how much better we are at swimming than they are! We don't normally need to, but we *can* swim up to twenty-five miles an hour.) That's why I've never actually seen a lava field myself, but of course one hears about these things thanks to what your greatly admired Carl Gustav Jung described as 'universal consciousness'. Ann, however, when she walked there with difficulty, was absolutely fascinated by the huge variety of patterns that had been formed by the lava before it solidified and she just couldn't stop taking photographs. She decided later that she'd better delete most of them for fear of running out of space on the memory card, but she couldn't delete this one that she was sure was a dog! Basically the only thing that can grow on these very rough, hard, fields, before they break down into soil, which of course takes ages and ages, is the lava cactus, so no wonder it's difficult to walk on. When the going had got particularly tough, the experienced Galápagos guide decided to entertain them all by almost disappearing into a hole.

'Dog'

'Rope' lava

Lava cactus

Guide in hole

Now, returning for a moment to the question of the current alarming state of the world, one of the things that feeds people's pessimism and gloom is all of the media's addiction to reporting bad news. Of course one shouldn't run away from the facts, but everyone would feel a lot better if there were greater emphasis on *good* news. It's not that there's a shortage of that, if one knows where to look. Although it's unfortunately only a quarterly, the only newspaper that our scribe really likes reading is 'Positive News'. This paper refuses to publish anything that isn't encouraging or inspiring, and it can be wonderful to read in it about the truly worthwhile things that people (often remarkably young people) are achieving all over the world. Of course present-day light workers and spiritual teachers do claim that many evolved souls are now incarnating into the new generation, and that is easier to believe when one reads about some of these youngsters' remarkable achievements.

By the way, do you think that Jung believed in reincarnation? Ann's late teacher, the distinguished Dr. Roger Woolger, who started as a Jungian psychotherapist before creating his own, highly individual, form of therapy that he eventually termed Deep Memory Process, believed that he probably did deep down, but that it wasn't appropriate for him to say so in the climate of his time. Woolger also had a private theory of his own that Jung might actually himself have been a reincarnation of Goethe. There was an unproven legend in the Jung family that Carl Gustav's grandfather had been an illegitimate son of Goethe, and Jung was profoundly influenced by Goethe's Faust, which he had memorised while still at school. An interesting notion, isn't it?

One thing that I haven't mentioned about our island's more recent history is that, because of human intervention, we have been infested by both goats and rats, which has had a really devastating effect. A lot has already been done to eliminate them all, but it is still an ongoing process and of course costs an absolutely horrendous amount of money. So any help that you could give would be immensely appreciated. Now I'll end with a warning and a plea because there is another problem that affects us sea lions personally. It's plastic bottles! I know that many of you now have huge problems with litter in your own countries, which is a disgrace because there's absolutely no excuse for it when there are plenty of litter bins around; it's yet another symptom of people not caring enough about others. Here, however, such things really are a huge danger to us. All the Galápagos guides always warn the people they're escorting about it, but one day Ann's bottle fell out of its holder while she was doing an awkward climb and it rolled out of her reach. Luckily a more agile member of the group was able to retrieve it, but that might not always happen. Most of you are very conscientious and cooperate with the guides by picking up any odd bits of plastic that you notice, but occasionally carelessness or accidents occur, so please be on the lookout. Thank you very much indeed!

Note

1   In Indian tradition, Earth's history is divided into 'yugas' (ages), each of which lasts a very long time indeed. *The Kali Yuga*, which is now coming to an end, is said to be the one in which all the evil that has been wrought for so long is coming to the surface in order for the Earth to be cleansed. There is no need to look very far for evidence of this!

A SPIDER'S TALE

The spider's technique of capture – tying up the prey caught in its web with its silken thread – would make it a symbol of maternity. The spider is the Mother-Enemy who enfolds and engulfs us, who wants to make us re-renter the womb from which we have come; to bind us tightly, so that we return to the impotence of infancy, and she can take us back into her power.

Sam Magavern ('PRIMO LEVI'S UNIVERSE:
A Writer's Journey')

Hullo, it's nice to meet you! I'm a Galapagos zigzag spider, but the official name for me is Neoscona cooksoni. That's all a bit of a mouthful, though, isn't it?, so you might just prefer to call me Zigzag or Ziggie. Anyway, I have a rather important question for you: why is it that so many members of your race are arachnophobic? The Collins Concise Dictionary's definition of this word is 'an *abnormal* [my underlining] fear of spiders', which implies that a fear of spiders is normal. Why? Nobody likes flies because they're unclean and can spread disease. Yet we remove flies from people's houses by consuming them, so why should it be considered normal to fear *us*? One theory I've heard, but I really don't know whether it's true, is that our race have come originally from another planet – that we're basically 'aliens' here and that's why so many people on Earth have a real horror of us. You might possibly reply "Well, if that's the case, why isn't the memory of where you originally came from in your genetic memory and consequently in your spidery consciousness?" If so, my retort to that is "Everyone, and every thing, in the universe (or maybe universes! Have you been following Professor Brian Cox on BBC television recently?) has come originally from God (or the Source, or whatever you like to call it), but how many people have forgotten that? In many cases forgotten it to the extent of becoming complete atheists."

Brian Cox is – quite rightly because he is very intelligent besides being a good TV presenter – extremely popular in Britain at the moment (Ann and David's mathematician son admires him enormously), and I believe he is doing a very good job in trying to encourage people to think about the future of the planet being in their hands. But it seems to me a great shame that people like him completely ignore things for which there is very well documented evidence. Atheist scientists such as Richard Dawkins are just the same: they insist that the material world that can actually be seen, if not touched, is all that there is, despite the many books that have been published by people with personal experience of the afterlife or out-of-body experiences. The best known of these just at the moment is probably *PROOF OF HEAVEN* [1] by a renowned, previously non-believing, American neuro-surgeon. As for the existence of extra-terrestrials, which Brian Cox clearly denies since he seems to think that you human beings are "alone in the universe", there is absolutely masses of well documented information about sightings of UFOs and so on. Why is that governments etc. always want to suppress all these interesting stories? What are they afraid of? Being attacked? In actual fact a more realistic view is that the Earth is being carefully watched and guarded by 'outsiders' who really care about what happens here.

Apparently it's just been in the news in Britain that Stephen Hawking has predicted the likelihood of computers developing minds of their own and the human race becoming extinct! That's another example of a very intelligent man who nevertheless fails to appreciate the reality of the soul. Whatever is achieved by a computer will only be the consequence of the *human* brain that created it in the first place, and no human brain, however good, will ever find a way to instill a soul into a computer. And without a soul (or a heart!) there can be no feelings. Who would like to live in a world with no feelings?

Of course atheists and agnostics will rediscover the truth about immortality eventually, but they could save themselves some time going 'home' if they became convinced of it *before* dying. That's because (as Ann explained in one of her previous books[2]), when people die they find what they expect to find, i.e. a Christian will encounter Jesus, a Muslim Mohamed and so on, but an atheist will initially encounter only nothingness, since they don't believe that there *is* anything apart from this one life. When Ann was a student and a keen member of the Bristol

University Catholic Society, she joined a little group of fellow Catholics who held meetings led by a radical, left-wing Dominican named Matthew Rigby. Unlike their predecessors who were largely responsible for the horrors of the Inquisition that was held against such people as the unfairly maligned and greatly misunderstood Cathars, present-day Dominicans tend to be open-minded philosophers, and this "Father Matt", as Ann and her friends knew him, was a great admirer of Bertrand Russell. He (that's Fr. Matt as well as Russell!) must be long dead by now, but Ann has a vivid memory of him saying about Russell "I believe that, when he died, he will have gone straight to Heaven and, when he met the Almighty face to face, it must have given him an almighty shock!" Now, however, Ann feels that Russell's "shock" won't have been instantaneous; according to the sort of works that she studies these days, it takes time – and help from other more aware souls – for them to wake up to the (hopefully pleasant!) surprise of finding that it's death rather than the afterlife that isn't real[3].

But going back to us now, it's true that *some* spiders (I'm not one of them) are venomous to human beings, but your chances of being poisoned by a spider are very slim indeed. Many people believe that fears such as these are innate – that human beings are born with them. This may be true of snakes (which so often *are* venomous), but studies have shown that on the whole young children *learn* their fears from watching the behaviour of adults. One thing that *is* certain, however, is that spiders have been the focus of fears, stories and mythologies of various cultures for hundreds, or rather thousands, of years.

Ann, my scribe, is not herself arachnophobic – nor has she in her therapy practice ever treated anyone for that particular phobia (though she has dealt successfully with other phobias, such as claustrophobia) – but her daughter *is* arachnophobic, and one Christmas Alice greatly welcomed the present of a special gadget for removing spiders from her abode without harming them. In fact Ann now wishes that she'd bought one for herself too and regrets not remembering the name of the catalogue she found it in. That's not because she minds seeing spiders, but simply because she thinks the webs make the house look a bit dirty and uncared for. She says it's not at all the same outside, that spiders' webs can look quite beautiful on grass or fences when they're covered in dew or frost; but when she saw *me*, hanging resplendently, alone, on a tree on my precious Galápagos island, she was mind blown. And it wasn't my web that blew her mind,

Spider

but the appearance of my body, which happens to be a dazzling blue (her favourite shade of her favourite colour), and there's also an amazing pattern on my back, which I suppose is how I got my nickname of zigzag. Ann exclaimed "Look! That spider's so beautiful it ought to be a brooch!" I was naturally very flattered, as I was by her numerous attempts to photograph me. That wasn't easy when there was a slight wind blowing, and she was afraid of getting left behind and losing the rest of the group, but fortunately there was someone else in her group who was more successful with her camera, and so this picture appears here thanks to Ann Titterington from Belfast.

Another part of the myth around spiders concerns precisely our bodies: to you who are so very differently shaped, the part of our body that houses our stomach no doubt appears to be rather 'outsize' compared with our small head and somewhat spindly legs. The great Italian writer, Primo Levi, who survived Auschwitz so amazingly, appears to have been arachnophobic at least in his childhood, for he recounts with horror, in a short essay entitled 'Fear of Spiders', his boyhood "collision" with the Gustave Doré illustration of Arachne for Dante's *Inferno*. This etching of the young girl who dared to challenge Minerva in the art of weaving is indeed somewhat horrific, but it is totally unfair on us spiders – as is this whole concept of the mother as enemy!

Of course it's true that human mothers *can* be over-possessive; letting go is the hardest thing for most parents of the human species (we spiders, insects and other non-human species tend to be better at it (if 'better' is the right word to use here!), but it is also one of the most important. My scribe and her husband knew someone whose widowed mother had followed him to Cambridge when he became a student there, then moved to the university town in which he obtained a lectureship, and the poor man only married at the age of forty-six, after his mother's death. It is natural and important for mothers to care deeply about their children, but the caring should never involve clinging.

In the case of John Ruskin, the renowned nineteenth century English writer, art critic and painter, *both* his parents appear to have been even worse than the mother of Ann and David's acquaintance, and they were very likely at least partly responsible for the failure of Ruskin's marriage to Effie Gray. The wonderful actor Emma Thompson (who also has a brief mention in one of my scribe's books[4]) has now taken to screen writing as well, and in her film entitled *Effie Gray*, the eponymous heroine is very well depicted in her suffering in the Ruskin household, and though her subsequent marriage to the painter Millais does not form part of the film, their falling in love right under Ruskin's nose is very movingly portrayed. Since her first marriage was never consummated, Effie was ultimately able to get it annulled, and of particular interest to Ann is the fact that one of the eight children of her second marriage was Alice, whose married name was Stuart Worsley. The reason for our scribe's interest is that Alice Stuart Worsley was not only a friend of the great English composer Edward Elgar[4], but also for a while his 'muse', to whom he gave the nickname of Windflower. The ideal image for any mother should be 'nurturer' rather than 'enemy', and that's certainly how we spiders (I'm sure like most of you) would prefer to be regarded!

Anyway, who are you Westerners to talk about 'fat stomachs' nowadays?! Isn't obesity one of your biggest problems at the moment? Certainly in Britain I've heard that it's costing your national health service a large fortune – money that could surely be better spent on, for instance, care for the elderly. According to the latest English Longitudinal Study of Ageing report, in 2012 one third of women over fifty and twenty-eight per cent of men were obese. And isn't it a scandal that so many people are making themselves ill by being overweight while in other parts of the world starvation and malnutrition are massive problems for millions? It used to be the US that was notorious for obesity, yet now Europe is apparently catching up quite rapidly. How unnecessary when all you would need to do to eradicate the problem would be to follow the example of the natural world by not eating more than you really need. Were the frigates you were admiring so much the other day overweight? Or have you ever seen a really fat ant? Sometimes a certain member of our species might *look* "horribly fat" to you, but that doesn't mean that it's out of proportion or unhealthy. It's true that dogs that live with fat people are often overweight too, but can you blame *them* for that? Domestic dogs just eat what they're given and, if the food that's put in front of them is overly tempting, it's only natural that they should indulge in it.

Now, while we're on the subject of human beings, it's perhaps time that you learnt a bit about those who inhabit these islands. Since the Galápagos officially belong to Ecuador, it is to be expected that its occupants, or most of them anyway, should be Spanish speaking. Historically the islands were used by Ecuador as a penal colony – a bit better than being shut up in prison I suppose! – but I'm glad to say that that has long since changed, and in 1998 a law was passed to make it more difficult for both Ecuadorians and foreigners to settle here. By the year 2000 the population had reached 20,000, which was a twenty-fold increase in just fifty years and, with an expansion of seven per cent per annum, these islands have at present the fastest growing population of all the Ecuadorian provinces. The capital, which has the lengthy name of Puerto Baquerizo Moreno and is on the island of San Cristóbal (St. Christopher to you), has a population of nearly four and a quarter thousand, but the largest town is Puerto Ayora on Santa Cruz. That, as visitors here will normally discover, is connected to the airport on Baltra by ferry and road, and so it is the normal point of departure for boats such as the ones used by the group we have been talking about. (Baltra, by the way, has nothing much on it apart from the airport except cacti. Some of our land has developed lush pastures that are ideal for cattle grazing on top of their lava base, but that takes a very long time and, as you've already heard, fresh water is in short supply here.)

Some tourists understandably prefer the luxury of staying on land in hotels, and the islands of Santa Cruz, Isabela, San Cristóbal and Floreana have between them a good choice of hotels of different standards. Floreana, by the way, is particularly famous for its Barrel Post Office, which dates from 1792. The tradition (dating of course from the times when seafarers had no other way of getting their letters to their home countries) is for people to go to the barrel not only to post their own letters, but also to look through those that are in there already and take out any that they think they will be able to deliver themselves by hand. Nowadays it's regarded as a bit of fun, and it can save postage – or even give someone the chance of making a new friend – though it does have to be said that some people break the rules and resort to putting stamps on and posting the correspondence once they're back in their own countries. That's what Ann eventually did somewhat reluctantly, but, even though her daughter has yet to receive her card, she was pleasantly surprised at how efficiently the system worked. The card that this couple sent to their own home arrived within days of their return, and a number of their friends thanked them for their cards shortly afterwards, with at least a couple having been delivered by hand.

Barrel letter box

Those who opt to sleep on land have of course the choice of numerous excursions, including boat trips to other islands. Although immigration is now restricted, tourist numbers are not, since our income is largely dependent upon them. Rather sadly, the boom of recent years has resulted in many inhabitants turning from agriculture to working in the tourist trade, and so, while the Galápagos islanders used to be self-sufficient, a lot of food now has to be imported from the mainland. This has increased the danger of the introduction of aggressive species that can become potential threats to the survival of ecosystems and species native and endemic to the islands. The Directorate of the Galápagos National Park consequently now takes as a priority support for management activities in agricultural areas that are aimed at the control and eradication of these threats. I'm glad to say that I and my fellows are not one of the threats! Nor are we the only spiders to be found here. Darwin, who was fascinated by "bugs, insects and spiders" from his early boyhood, noticed when he was on board the famous Beagle, thousands of tiny, dusty red spiders floating on board, "their silk threads trapping them in the rigging". He was also interested to note during his stay in our islands that he only found twenty-nine different types of beetle – about half of what would normally be expected for an archipelago of this size.

Because of the shortage of insects for pollination, most Galápagos plants are self-pollinating, and therefore their flowers don't need to have

Galapagos flowers

Ecuadorian market

Cicada

'showy' colours. This explains why almost all the flowers here are either yellow or white, which, as you can see in this photo, might seem a bit boring compared to some of the glorious colours that can be seen on the mainland of Ecuador, such as the flowers for sale in this market. Most of the groups that come here are too busy gawping at the larger wildlife to bother much with either flowers or insects, but Ann was rather pleased with this photo that she managed to take of a cicada.

Of greater interest to most of them, though, are the reptiles, shellfish and fish of different colours, but in order to see these last well, you have to be keen to go snorkelling at a certain distance from the shore, which doesn't suit non-swimmers like Ann's husband David. But both of them were very impressed by the size and colour of the Sally Lightfoot Crabs, which they found considerably less unattractive than the marine iguanas. These strange-looking creatures, which are much smaller than their counterparts found further inland, which can easily reach four-five metres in length, are unique in having developed the ability to swim in the sea. They live on algae, for which they have to dive deep, and they have webbed toes and a tail suitable for swimming, and long claws to help them climb up rocks. During the hot season, which is December to May, they can survive for up to an hour in the water, but when Darwin was experimenting and threw them into the sea in October, he found that they couldn't last there for any more than twenty minutes. Henry Nicholls, in his excellent book[5], points out that when Darwin talked about marine

Sally Lightfoot Crab

iguanas as being "imps of darkness", he was actually quoting George Byron, the captain of HMS Blonde writing on Fernandina in 1825, a whole ten years before the Beagle's arrival. But perhaps the most notable thing of all about these "imps of darkness" is their rather unpleasant habit of continuously spitting. You should never take it personally, though; it's just that, having only sea water to drink, they've had to develop a way of getting rid of the excess salt that they've swallowed.

Marine iguanas

Land iguana

Anyway, if you want to know more about other Galápagos creatures, you can always look elsewhere. Let's get back to spiders now! Has it occurred to you to wonder why 'fear of spiders' should be designated by the word 'arachnophobic'? Well, whereas your English word comes from Old English, 'spitra', this adjective comes from the Greek for spider, which is 'arakhne', while the noun comes from the Latin 'araneus'. Romance languages more often have Latin roots than Greek, but in this case there seems to be a close connection between those two ancient languages (the Collins dictionary calls it being "cognate with"). Our name in Spanish ('araña') is identical to the Portuguese ('aranha'); it's just that the Spanish make the 'ng' sound by substituting a 'tilde' on top of the 'n' for the 'g' before it, while the Portuguese drop the 'g' and make the 'ng' sound by putting an 'h' *after* the 'n'. In French the word has developed one step further: they always tend to change a final 'a' into 'ée', and in this word, oddly, the middle 'a' sound has also changed into an 'ée' ('eh' to you English speakers!). So in French I'm called an 'araignée', while in German it's a completely different word again – 'spinne'. I suppose they call us that because of the fact that we spin. (Germans tend to be very logical, despite the big claim of the French in that regard! Who was it said "Ce qui n'est pas logique n'est pas français."?) But more about webs in a moment.

Of non-English languages, only Italian (which has dropped the initial 'a' and made the word 'ragno'. Is that laziness? I'm sure many Italians are more hardworking than Berlusconi ever was!) has kept the word masculine, as it was in Latin (though maybe there you could also have had an 'aranea'. What do you think? My Latin's never been *that* brilliant.) Don't you think the Italians are wrong to do that? Aren't we females *much* more important than the males? If we didn't lay eggs, there just wouldn't be any more spiders! It's true that we do need a male, very briefly, for copulation, but after that's over and done with, the only thing he's good for is a meal. Those can be quite hard to come by at times, especially if there aren't many flies around. Not that we *always* succeed in consuming our mates; sometimes they escape too quickly, and sometimes they fool us by pretending to be dead (who wants dead food? – yuck!). Primo Levi, the great Italian writer whom I mentioned before, wrote a rather amusing interview between a journalist and a spider[6], which, by the way, makes me think that he *did* ultimately get over his arachnophobia. In it he is taking the mickey a bit, by making out that absolutely all a spider is ever interested in is food, but what I *do* like about Levi's little piece is that he shows appreciation of both our skill and our patience when it comes to web making. Incidentally Levi's 'suicide' has never been proven. After all, anyone could fall down a flight of stairs, and Levi always insisted that his experiences of Auschwitz had left him with an even stronger will to live. *Everyone* (especially Holocaust deniers!) should read his autobiographical book[7] if they haven't done so already. When Ann (who perished in a different concentration camp in one of her previous lives[8]) visited Auschwitz, she felt completely incapable of writing about it, yet Levi managed to record his experiences in the most telling way, and not all that long afterwards either.

But I've left what is perhaps the most important point about my species till last! I've so far only mentioned webs in passing, yet their significance is obviously immense, isn't it? You who use computers regularly (and in that I include of course tablets (not the sort that you swallow!) and these amazing new-fangled mobile phones (or cell phones if you're American) that do virtually everything apart from the washing up) will very likely type "www" into them several times a day. And you all know that that means 'world wide web'. So, even if you *are* arachnophobic, you *have* to be grateful to us for this wonderful invention! You might accuse us of having invented it purely for our own purposes, as a means of catching what we need to eat, yet in your adoption of it you are recognising, if only subconsciously, that absolutely everything, in all the worlds, both seen and unseen, is interconnected.

In Hinduism, and I believe in Chinese mythology too, though they would doubtless have their own vocabulary for it, 'Indra's web' (or net, but whatever word you use, it's pinched from our invention) is extended to represent the interconnectedness of the entire universe. To quote Wikipedia (one of the most useful things your "www" has produced, even though the internet is also, alas, plagued by pornography!): "Far away in the heavenly abode of the great god Indra, there is a wonderful net which has been hung by some cunning artificer in such a manner that it stretches out infinitely in all directions. In accordance with the extravagant tastes of deities, the artificer has hung a single glittering jewel in each "eye" of the net, and since the net itself is infinite in dimension, the jewels are infinite in number." Well, I said earlier that Ann was often entranced by the sight of frost or dew on spider's webs and they can easily remind one of jewels. Wikipedia continues: "There hang the jewels, glittering "like" stars in the first magnitude, a wonderful sight to behold. If we now arbitrarily select one of these jewels for inspection and look closely at it, we will discover that in its polished surface there are reflected *all* the other jewels in the net, infinite in number. Not only that, but each of the jewels reflected in this one jewel is also reflecting all the other jewels, so that there is an infinite reflecting process occurring." And Wikipedia also says that this metaphor plays an essential role in the Chinese Huayan school, where it is used to describe the interpenetration of microcosmos and macrocosmos.

All that is the positive side of the web mythology, but you, alas, over millennia, have also given it a negative connotation. In Hinduism, centuries older of course than either Christianity or Islam, the word 'maya' has been given various definitions, but the most commonly accepted one is probably equivalent to the English word 'illusion' ('ilusión' in Spanish). Because, according to Buddhism as well as Hinduism, the only *reality* is to be found in worlds *other* than this physical one. Your Shakespeare put it well in his play *As You Like It*, when he said "All the world's a stage, and all the men and women merely players. They have their exits and their entrances; and one man in his time plays many parts…" Though I find it hard to imagine at the moment, I myself will very likely not come back as a spider next time round, and you who have supposedly reached the 'pinnacle' of evolution by achieving human bodies, don each time not only a new physical body but also a different personality. Both of these are impermanent, but *that's* not the negative aspect of this question – after all, one can say that "the only constant is change" – what *is* negative is how you've come to equate this 'maya', or the acting of different parts, with a web from which there is "no escape".

Buddhists depict this as 'the wheel of *samsara*' – the repeated return to Earth, where we endeavour to pay off debts as well as learn new lessons, but also at the same time seem constantly to incur *new* debts, which in turn create the need to come back yet again – but is this notion of "being trapped forever" in fact just another illusion? Well, the good news I'd now like to give you is that you all both can and *will* ultimately escape from the web – once you have recognised the nature of the illusion that you have given yourselves over so many centuries and over so many, utterly varied, lifetimes. You can call it *Enlightenment* if you wish, or *Moksha* meaning 'Liberation', but its name is unimportant. What *is* important is the realisation that this is what you are after. Ann noticed a good analogy for it in the chorus of a song by the American singer/song writer Randy Newman, broadcast from London's Wigmore Hall on 23 November 2014 (Sathya Sai Baba's birthday!). The singer was the distinguished German counter-tenor Andreas Scholl, the song was called 'In Germany before the War' and the chorus went "I am looking at the river, but I'm thinking of the sea." For what are we all but tiny streams, brooks, tributaries or mighty rivers flowing towards the ocean that is God/the Source? Whether or not we actually remember that our aim is to merge once more with the Sea from which we originally came, that memory is buried somewhere deep in our subconscious, waiting to resurface when the time is right.

And what is the best way of encouraging that knowledge to resurface? You don't need to be a great sage or saint to achieve it. All that is necessary is quite simply to lead the best life that you possibly can, unselfishly, caring for others, but at the same time not undervaluing your*self*. By finding and using your individual talents, and recognising your *own* divinity. In Christianity a lot of the original scriptures were not included in the Bible that's used today, and the early Christians' belief in reincarnation was stamped out in 553 AD by the Council of Constantinople, but the fact of not recognising their own divinity or accepting multiple lives needn't be a barrier to present-day Christians who sincerely try to live by Jesus' example. It's not what you believe that matters, but the way you live your life, and Brian Cox, Stephen Hawking and those who go along with their views might well be leading more worthwhile lives than are many religious people.

Dr. Jude Currivan strove to give us HOPE in her book of that title, so let us keep *that* as our eternal reality rather than the 'illusions' of wealth, power or fame. I hope I may have succeeded in curing some of you of your arachnophobia but, even if I haven't, I hope that I've at least given you something to think about. Now what better way can I end both what I have to say to you, and this little book, by quoting from our beloved Dalai Lama? "As human beings we each have a responsibility to care for humanity. Expressing concern for others brings inner strength and deep satisfaction. As social animals, human beings need friendship, but friendship doesn't come from wealth and power, but from showing compassion and concern for others."

With love and best wishes from me, Ziggie, and also from our other four heroines and heroes.

Notes

1   *PROOF OF HEAVEN – A Neurosurgeon's Journey* in the Afterlife, Dr. Eben Alexander, Simon & Schuster, USA, 2012.

2   See *DELAYED DEPARTURE – A Beginner's Guide to Soul Rescue*, Ann Merivale, 6th Books, 2013.

3   *THICKER THAN BLOOD? – A Fresh Look at Adoption, Fostering and Step Families*, Ann Merivale, 6th Books, 2015.

4   *LIFE WITHOUT ELGAR – A Tale of a Journeying Soul*, Ann Merivale, 6th Books, 2014.

5   *THE GALAPAGOS – A Natural History*, Henry Nicholls, Profile Books, London, 2014.

6   L'intervista is one of the sections in Primo Levi's little book L'ultimo Natale di guerra, Einaudi Tascabili, Turin, 2002. Unfortunately I have not been able to find an English translation of the book, but in this delightful interview with a spider by a journalist, the spider asks the journalist whether he is edible and whether an interview (a new word for her!) is something that she would be able to eat.

7   *IF THIS IS A MAN* and *THE TRUCE*, Primo Levi, translated by Stuart Woolf, first published by Penguin, 1979.

8   *KARMIC RELEASE – Journeying Back to the Self*, Ann Merivale, Sai Towers Publishing, Bangalore, 2006.

BY THE SAME AUTHOR

KARMIC RELEASE – Journeying Back to the Self, Sai Towers
Publishing, Bangalore, India, 2006, ISBN 81-86822-66-6

SOULS UNITED – The Power of Divine Connection, Llewellyn
Worldwide, USA, 2009, ISBN 978-0-7387-1528-5

DISCOVERING THE LIFE PLAN – Eleven Steps to Your Destiny,
6th Books, 2012, ISBN 978-84694-821-3

DELAYED DEPARTURE – A Beginner's Guide to Soul Rescue,
6th Books, 2013, ISBN 978-1-78279-011-2

LIFE WITHOUT ELGAR – A Tale of a Journeying Soul, 6th Books,
2014, ISBN 978-1-78279-526-1

*THICKER THAN BLOOD? – A Fresh Look at Adoption, Fostering and
Step Families*, 6th Books, ISBN 978-1-78279-836-1